INTUITIVELY CONNECTED

SET IN SOUL

THIS JOURNAL BELONGS TO

DEDICATED TO MY SPIRIT.
I TRUST OUR CONNECTION.
MAY WE ALWAYS BE BEST
FRIENDS. THANK YOU GOD.

TABLE OF CONTENTS

HOW TO USE THIS JOURNAL

You know you are in a particular spiritual season, but you cannot seem to figure out what season it is. You know that you are more aware, maybe a bit more sensitive, and that you feel different. Maybe every year, at a certain time, your spirit or body requires something different from you. Maybe you've taken notice of a particular time in your life or particular time of the year when anything you claimed was yours came into existence effortlessly. Or maybe you noticed you're just not as talkative now and you prefer being alone or observing others rather than socializing. You just can't put your finger on it. You try to figure out what's going on, why you feel this way, and so forth. The only thing you do know is that you are in a season. You may not be exactly sure what you should be doing or when this started, but you are connected. Your spirit is connected to The Most High, and there is an assignment for you this season. There is something that needs your attention. It's time for you "to do" or "not do" something, and this is where your journal comes in. This journal will aid you in exploring and accepting your season. It is time to give your season a name and pay close attention to it, as every season is a seed for the next.

Intuitively Connected was created to guide you through your current season and help you understand past seasons. This journal provides daily spiritual questions that will help you to gain clarity. This is your time to attend to your needs and maneuver through any confusion, chaos, and distractions that are keeping you from understanding what is being presented to you. This may be your first time feeling this way or the first time you are trying to understand what you need. It is recommended that you fill out this journal daily and truly give your spirit the time it needs to lead you to where you ultimately should be within and outside of yourself. It is recommended that you fill out this journal before bedtime and that you pair this practice with prayer and meditation. This is your season to be in touch with what is needed from you to finally move in the direction of your prayers. Now is the time to pay attention and answer your calling. You are intuitively connected in mind, body, and spirit.

SPIRITUAL SHIFTING
QUESTIONS

SPIRITUAL SHIFTING QUESTIONS

1/12/20
Currently I Feel:

The Emotions I've Been Feeling:

I Notice There Are Different Periods In My Life That:

I Tend To Repeat These Behaviors:

SPIRITUAL SHIFTING QUESTIONS

Around A Certain Time Of The Year I:

I Currently Get Motivated By:

Around This Time Of The Year My Body Feels:

I Am More Sensitive To:

Recent Changes I Am Noticing:

SPIRITUAL SHIFTING QUESTIONS

I Am Battling With:

I Know I'm Suppose To_____, But I Can't

_____.

I Am Being Called To:

When I Identify With Past Seasons In My Life, I Think:

Changes I Am Preparing For:

SPIRITUAL SHIFTING QUESTIONS

I Can No Longer Ignore:

Doors That Have Closed On Me:

Doors That Have Opened For Me:

Feelings Of Discomfort (State What You Think/Know Are Causing Those Feelings):

Opposition I Am Facing Within Myself And Others:

SPIRITUAL SHIFTING QUESTIONS

New Habits I Need To Take Up:

I Have Accepted:

Previous Seasons Have Lasted:

Previous Seasons Have Prepared Me For:

The Current Spiritual Climate Of What I Have Been Going Through And Feeling:

SPIRITUAL SHIFTING QUESTIONS

I Believe I Am Being Positioned For:

Internally I Am Hearing:

What I Am Not Understanding Is:

I Feel Released From:

What Is Changing Inside Of Me:

SPIRITUAL SHIFTING QUESTIONS

I Feel The Need To:

I Must Stay Clear From:

There Was A Time In My Life When:

This Is A Time In My Life When:

I Have A Deep Yearning For:

14

SPIRITUAL SHIFTING QUESTIONS

I Am Being Inspired By:

I Feel The Need To:

Intuitively, I Am:

These Things Have Been Happening (List Them):

'Coincidences' That I Have Been Noticing:

SPIRITUAL SHIFTING QUESTIONS

My Sleeping Patterns Have Changed By:

I Have Gained Interest In:

I Have Lost Interest In:

I Feel Connected To:

I Have Become More In Sync With:

SPIRITUAL SHIFTING QUESTIONS

I Have Become More:

I Have Become Less:

My Personality Is Now:

I Feel Like My Spirit Requires:

I Connect With:

SPIRITUAL SHIFTING QUESTIONS

I No Longer Connect With:

HOLD ON,
LET'S CONNECT

HOLD ON, LET'S CONNECT

Date: Season (Name It):   Days In This Season:

I Feel: My Spirit Feels:

Today I Was Pushed To: I Spent Time With God By:

Today I Felt That I Was Being Pulled   Questions I Have:
Away From:

This Season, I Am Seeing: Answers To Questions The Spirit
                                       Provided:

Today I Meditated On:

                                       I Spent The Night Before:

Today I Noticed:

                                       Last Night's Dream/Today's Daydream:

Today's Eureka Moment:

Last Night's Sleep Was _____.

I FEEL LIKE IT'S TIME TO ...

HOLD ON, LET'S CONNECT

Date: Season (Name It):   Days In This Season:

I Feel: My Spirit Feels:

Today I Was Pushed To: I Spent Time With God By:

Today I Felt That I Was Being Pulled   Questions I Have:
Away From:

This Season, I Am Seeing: Answers To Questions The Spirit
                                                Provided:

Today I Meditated On:

                                                I Spent The Night Before:

Today I Noticed:

                                                Last Night's Dream/Today's Daydream:

Today's Eureka Moment:

Last Night's Sleep Was _____.

HOLD ON, LET'S CONNECT

Date: Season (Name It):   Days In This Season:

I Feel: My Spirit Feels:

Today I Was Pushed To: I Spent Time With God By:

Today I Felt That I Was Being Pulled   Questions I Have:
Away From:

This Season, I Am Seeing: Answers To Questions The Spirit
                                                    Provided:

Today I Meditated On:
                                                    I Spent The Night Before:

Today I Noticed:
                                                    Last Night's Dream/Today's Daydream:

Today's Eureka Moment:

Last Night's Sleep Was _____.

CONNECTED NOTES

(Jot Down Your Thoughts Here)

HOLD ON, LET'S CONNECT

Date: Season (Name It):   Days In This Season:

I Feel:

My Spirit Feels:

Today I Was Pushed To:

I Spent Time With God By:

Today I Felt That I Was Being Pulled Away From:

Questions I Have:

This Season, I Am Seeing:

Answers To Questions The Spirit Provided:

Today I Meditated On:

I Spent The Night Before:

Today I Noticed:

Last Night's Dream/Today's Daydream:

Today's Eureka Moment:

Last Night's Sleep Was _____.

HOLD ON, LET'S CONNECT

Date: Season (Name It):   Days In This Season:

I Feel: My Spirit Feels:

Today I Was Pushed To: I Spent Time With God By:

Today I Felt That I Was Being Pulled   Questions I Have:
Away From:

This Season, I Am Seeing: Answers To Questions The Spirit
                                                  Provided:

Today I Meditated On:

                                                  I Spent The Night Before:

Today I Noticed:

                                                  Last Night's Dream/Today's Daydream:

Today's Eureka Moment:

Last Night's Sleep Was _____.

NOTHING THAT HAPPENS TO ME IS BY ACCIDENT.

SOME OF THE THINGS I'VE STOPPED DOING/ SAYING/WATCHING/ LISTENING ...

SOME OF THE THINGS I'VE STARTED DOING/ SAYING/WATCHING/ LISTENING ...

28

HOLD ON, LET'S CONNECT

Date: Season (Name It):   Days In This Season:

I Feel:

My Spirit Feels:

Today I Was Pushed To:

I Spent Time With God By:

Today I Felt That I Was Being Pulled Away From:

Questions I Have:

This Season, I Am Seeing:

Answers To Questions The Spirit Provided:

Today I Meditated On:

I Spent The Night Before:

Today I Noticed:

Last Night's Dream/Today's Daydream:

Today's Eureka Moment:

Last Night's Sleep Was _____.

HOLD ON, LET'S CONNECT

Date: Season (Name It):   Days In This Season:

I Feel: My Spirit Feels:

Today I Was Pushed To: I Spent Time With God By:

Today I Felt That I Was Being Pulled   Questions I Have:
Away From:

This Season, I Am Seeing: Answers To Questions The Spirit
                                                  Provided:

Today I Meditated On:

                                                  I Spent The Night Before:

Today I Noticed:

                                                  Last Night's Dream/Today's Daydream:

Today's Eureka Moment:

Last Night's Sleep Was _____.

CONNECTED NOTES

(Jot Down Your Thoughts Here)

HOLD ON, LET'S CONNECT

Date: Season (Name It):   Days In This Season:

I Feel: My Spirit Feels:

Today I Was Pushed To: I Spent Time With God By:

Today I Felt That I Was Being Pulled   Questions I Have:
Away From:

This Season, I Am Seeing: Answers To Questions The Spirit
                                                  Provided:

Today I Meditated On:

                                                  I Spent The Night Before:

Today I Noticed:

                                                  Last Night's Dream/Today's Daydream:

Today's Eureka Moment:

Last Night's Sleep Was _____.

HOLD ON, LET'S CONNECT

Date: Season (Name It):   Days In This Season:

I Feel: My Spirit Feels:

Today I Was Pushed To: I Spent Time With God By:

Today I Felt That I Was Being Pulled   Questions I Have:
Away From:

This Season, I Am Seeing: Answers To Questions The Spirit
                                                  Provided:

Today I Meditated On:

                                                  I Spent The Night Before:

Today I Noticed:

                                                  Last Night's Dream/Today's Daydream:

Today's Eureka Moment:

Last Night's Sleep Was _____.

FEELING
THANKFUL.

HOLD ON, LET'S CONNECT

Date: Season (Name It):   Days In This Season:

I Feel: My Spirit Feels:

Today I Was Pushed To: I Spent Time With God By:

Today I Felt That I Was Being Pulled   Questions I Have:
Away From:

This Season, I Am Seeing: Answers To Questions The Spirit
                                                     Provided:

Today I Meditated On:

                                                     I Spent The Night Before:

Today I Noticed:

                                                     Last Night's Dream/Today's Daydream:

Today's Eureka Moment:

Last Night's Sleep Was _____.

HOLD ON, LET'S CONNECT

Date: Season (Name It):   Days In This Season:

I Feel: | My Spirit Feels:

Today I Was Pushed To: | I Spent Time With God By:

Today I Felt That I Was Being Pulled | Questions I Have:
Away From:

This Season, I Am Seeing: | Answers To Questions The Spirit
                                             | Provided:

Today I Meditated On:

                                             | I Spent The Night Before:

Today I Noticed:

                                             | Last Night's Dream/Today's Daydream:

Today's Eureka Moment:

Last Night's Sleep Was _____.

HOLD ON, LET'S CONNECT

Date: Season (Name It):   Days In This Season:

I Feel: My Spirit Feels:

Today I Was Pushed To: I Spent Time With God By:

Today I Felt That I Was Being Pulled   Questions I Have:
Away From:

This Season, I Am Seeing: Answers To Questions The Spirit
                                                  Provided:

Today I Meditated On:

                                                  I Spent The Night Before:

Today I Noticed:

                                                  Last Night's Dream/Today's Daydream:

Today's Eureka Moment:

Last Night's Sleep Was _____.

HOLD ON, LET'S CONNECT

Date: Season (Name It):   Days In This Season:

I Feel: My Spirit Feels:

Today I Was Pushed To: I Spent Time With God By:

Today I Felt That I Was Being Pulled   Questions I Have:
Away From:

This Season, I Am Seeing: Answers To Questions The Spirit
                                           Provided:

Today I Meditated On:

                                           I Spent The Night Before:

Today I Noticed:

                                           Last Night's Dream/Today's Daydream:

Today's Eureka Moment:

Last Night's Sleep Was _____.

I MAY NOT KNOW EXACTLY WHAT IT IS, BUT I CAN FEEL SOMETHING HAPPENING.

I DON'T KEEP KEEP BAD COMPANY AROUND.

HOLD ON, LET'S CONNECT

Date: Season (Name It):   Days In This Season:

I Feel: | My Spirit Feels:

Today I Was Pushed To: | I Spent Time With God By:

Today I Felt That I Was Being Pulled | Questions I Have:
Away From:

This Season, I Am Seeing: | Answers To Questions The Spirit
                                       | Provided:

Today I Meditated On:

                                       | I Spent The Night Before:

Today I Noticed:

                                       | Last Night's Dream/Today's Daydream:

Today's Eureka Moment:

Last Night's Sleep Was _____.

CONNECTED NOTES

(Jot Down Your Thoughts Here)

HOLD ON, LET'S CONNECT

Date: Season (Name It):   Days In This Season:

I Feel: My Spirit Feels:

Today I Was Pushed To: I Spent Time With God By:

Today I Felt That I Was Being Pulled   Questions I Have:
Away From:

This Season, I Am Seeing: Answers To Questions The Spirit
                                                  Provided:

Today I Meditated On:

                                                  I Spent The Night Before:

Today I Noticed:

                                                  Last Night's Dream/Today's Daydream:

Today's Eureka Moment:

Last Night's Sleep Was _____.

HOLD ON, LET'S CONNECT

Date: Season (Name It):   Days In This Season:

I Feel: My Spirit Feels:

Today I Was Pushed To: I Spent Time With God By:

Today I Felt That I Was Being Pulled   Questions I Have:
Away From:

This Season, I Am Seeing: Answers To Questions The Spirit
                                             Provided:

Today I Meditated On:

                                             I Spent The Night Before:

Today I Noticed:

                                             Last Night's Dream/Today's Daydream:

Today's Eureka Moment:

Last Night's Sleep Was _____.

44

HOLD ON, LET'S CONNECT

Date: Season (Name It):   Days In This Season:

I Feel: My Spirit Feels:

Today I Was Pushed To: I Spent Time With God By:

Today I Felt That I Was Being Pulled   Questions I Have:
Away From:

This Season, I Am Seeing: Answers To Questions The Spirit
                                           Provided:

Today I Meditated On:

                                           I Spent The Night Before:

Today I Noticed:

                                           Last Night's Dream/Today's Daydream:

Today's Eureka Moment:

Last Night's Sleep Was _____.

TEN PRAYERS
I WOULD LIKE
ANSWERED

1.

2.

3.

4.

5.

6.

7.

8.

9.

10.

HOLD ON, LET'S CONNECT

Date: Season (Name It):   Days In This Season:

I Feel: My Spirit Feels:

Today I Was Pushed To: I Spent Time With God By:

Today I Felt That I Was Being Pulled   Questions I Have:
Away From:

This Season, I Am Seeing: Answers To Questions The Spirit
                                           Provided:

Today I Meditated On:

                                           I Spent The Night Before:

Today I Noticed:

                                           Last Night's Dream/Today's Daydream:

Today's Eureka Moment:

Last Night's Sleep Was _____.

HOLD ON, LET'S CONNECT

Date: Season (Name It):   Days In This Season:

I Feel: My Spirit Feels:

Today I Was Pushed To: I Spent Time With God By:

Today I Felt That I Was Being Pulled   Questions I Have:
Away From:

This Season, I Am Seeing: Answers To Questions The Spirit
                                                     Provided:

Today I Meditated On:

                                                     I Spent The Night Before:

Today I Noticed:

                                                     Last Night's Dream/Today's Daydream:

Today's Eureka Moment:

Last Night's Sleep Was _____.

HOLD ON, LET'S CONNECT

Date: Season (Name It):   Days In This Season:

I Feel: My Spirit Feels:

Today I Was Pushed To: I Spent Time With God By:

Today I Felt That I Was Being Pulled   Questions I Have:
Away From:

This Season, I Am Seeing: Answers To Questions The Spirit
                                           Provided:

Today I Meditated On:

                                           I Spent The Night Before:

Today I Noticed:

                                           Last Night's Dream/Today's Daydream:

Today's Eureka Moment:

Last Night's Sleep Was _____.

HOLD ON, LET'S CONNECT

Date: Season (Name It):   Days In This Season:

I Feel: My Spirit Feels:

Today I Was Pushed To: I Spent Time With God By:

Today I Felt That I Was Being Pulled   Questions I Have:
Away From:

This Season, I Am Seeing: Answers To Questions The Spirit
                                                     Provided:

Today I Meditated On:

                                                     I Spent The Night Before:

Today I Noticed:

                                                     Last Night's Dream/Today's Daydream:

Today's Eureka Moment:

Last Night's Sleep Was _____.

CONNECTED NOTES

(Jot Down Your Thoughts Here)

HOLD ON, LET'S CONNECT

Date: Season (Name It):   Days In This Season:

I Feel: There is a lesson in my current situation
                                     My Spirit Feels:

Today I Was Pushed To: I Spent Time With God By:

Today I Felt That I Was Being Pulled   Questions I Have:
Away From:

This Season, I Am Seeing: Answers To Questions The Spirit
                                     Provided:

Today I Meditated On:

                                     I Spent The Night Before:

Today I Noticed:

                                     Last Night's Dream/Today's Daydream:

Today's Eureka Moment:

Last Night's Sleep Was _____.

HOLD ON, LET'S CONNECT

Date: Season (Name It):   Days In This Season:

I Feel: My Spirit Feels:

Today I Was Pushed To: I Spent Time With God By:

Today I Felt That I Was Being Pulled   Questions I Have:
Away From:

This Season, I Am Seeing: Answers To Questions The Spirit
                                           Provided:

Today I Meditated On:

                                           I Spent The Night Before:

Today I Noticed:

                                           Last Night's Dream/Today's Daydream:

Today's Eureka Moment:

Last Night's Sleep Was _____.

THERE IS A LESSON IN MY CURRENT SITUATION.

HOLD ON, LET'S CONNECT

Date: Season (Name It):   Days In This Season:

I Feel: My Spirit Feels:

Today I Was Pushed To: I Spent Time With God By:

Today I Felt That I Was Being Pulled   Questions I Have:
Away From:

This Season, I Am Seeing: Answers To Questions The Spirit
                                                 Provided:

Today I Meditated On:

                                                 I Spent The Night Before:

Today I Noticed:

                                                 Last Night's Dream/Today's Daydream:

Today's Eureka Moment:

Last Night's Sleep Was _____.

HOLD ON, LET'S CONNECT

Date: Season (Name It):   Days In This Season:

I Feel: | My Spirit Feels:

Today I Was Pushed To: | I Spent Time With God By:

Today I Felt That I Was Being Pulled | Questions I Have:
Away From:

This Season, I Am Seeing: | Answers To Questions The Spirit
                                             | Provided:

Today I Meditated On:

                                             | I Spent The Night Before:

Today I Noticed:

                                             | Last Night's Dream/Today's Daydream:

Today's Eureka Moment:

Last Night's Sleep Was _____.

CONNECTED NOTES

(Jot Down Your Thoughts Here)

HOLD ON, LET'S CONNECT

Date: Season (Name It):   Days In This Season:

I Feel: | My Spirit Feels:

Today I Was Pushed To: | I Spent Time With God By:

Today I Felt That I Was Being Pulled | Questions I Have:
Away From:

This Season, I Am Seeing: | Answers To Questions The Spirit
                                        | Provided:

Today I Meditated On:

                                        | I Spent The Night Before:

Today I Noticed:

                                        | Last Night's Dream/Today's Daydream:

Today's Eureka Moment:

Last Night's Sleep Was _____.

SO MANY WONDERFUL THINGS ARE HAPPENING IN MY STILLNESS.

HOLD ON, LET'S CONNECT

Date: Season (Name It):   Days In This Season:

I Feel: My Spirit Feels:

Today I Was Pushed To: I Spent Time With God By:

Today I Felt That I Was Being Pulled   Questions I Have:
Away From:

This Season, I Am Seeing: Answers To Questions The Spirit
                                                     Provided:

Today I Meditated On:

                                                     I Spent The Night Before:

Today I Noticed:

                                                     Last Night's Dream/Today's Daydream:

Today's Eureka Moment:

Last Night's Sleep Was _____.

HOLD ON, LET'S CONNECT

Date: Season (Name It):   Days In This Season:

I Feel: My Spirit Feels:

Today I Was Pushed To: I Spent Time With God By:

Today I Felt That I Was Being Pulled   Questions I Have:
Away From:

This Season, I Am Seeing: Answers To Questions The Spirit
                                             Provided:

Today I Meditated On:

                                             I Spent The Night Before:

Today I Noticed:

                                             Last Night's Dream/Today's Daydream:

Today's Eureka Moment:

Last Night's Sleep Was _____.

HOLD ON, LET'S CONNECT

Date: Season (Name It):   Days In This Season:

I Feel: My Spirit Feels:

Today I Was Pushed To: I Spent Time With God By:

Today I Felt That I Was Being Pulled   Questions I Have:
Away From:

This Season, I Am Seeing: Answers To Questions The Spirit
                                                 Provided:

Today I Meditated On:

                                                 I Spent The Night Before:

Today I Noticed:

                                                 Last Night's Dream/Today's Daydream:

Today's Eureka Moment:

Last Night's Sleep Was _____.

HOLD ON, LET'S CONNECT

Date: Season (Name It):   Days In This Season:

I Feel: My Spirit Feels:

Today I Was Pushed To: I Spent Time With God By:

Today I Felt That I Was Being Pulled   Questions I Have:
Away From:

This Season, I Am Seeing: Answers To Questions The Spirit
                                                Provided:

Today I Meditated On:

                                                I Spent The Night Before:

Today I Noticed:

                                                Last Night's Dream/Today's Daydream:

Today's Eureka Moment:

Last Night's Sleep Was _____.

I'VE BEEN
DREAMING ...

CONNECTED NOTES

(Jot Down Your Thoughts Here)

HOLD ON, LET'S CONNECT

Date: Season (Name It):   Days In This Season:

I Feel: My Spirit Feels:

Today I Was Pushed To: I Spent Time With God By:

Today I Felt That I Was Being Pulled   Questions I Have:
Away From:

This Season, I Am Seeing: Answers To Questions The Spirit
                                               Provided:

Today I Meditated On:

                                               I Spent The Night Before:

Today I Noticed:

                                               Last Night's Dream/Today's Daydream:

Today's Eureka Moment:

Last Night's Sleep Was _____.

HOLD ON, LET'S CONNECT

Date: Season (Name It):   Days In This Season:

I Feel: My Spirit Feels:

Today I Was Pushed To: I Spent Time With God By:

Today I Felt That I Was Being Pulled   Questions I Have:
Away From:

This Season, I Am Seeing: Answers To Questions The Spirit
                                                    Provided:

Today I Meditated On:

                                                    I Spent The Night Before:

Today I Noticed:

                                                    Last Night's Dream/Today's Daydream:

Today's Eureka Moment:

Last Night's Sleep Was _____.

HOLD ON, LET'S CONNECT

Date: Season (Name It):   Days In This Season:

I Feel: My Spirit Feels:

Today I Was Pushed To: I Spent Time With God By:

Today I Felt That I Was Being Pulled   Questions I Have:
Away From:

This Season, I Am Seeing: Answers To Questions The Spirit
                                                 Provided:

Today I Meditated On:

                                                 I Spent The Night Before:

                        In my time alone, I am not really alone.

Today I Noticed:

                                                 Last Night's Dream/Today's Daydream:

Today's Eureka Moment:

Last Night's Sleep Was _____.

HOLD ON, LET'S CONNECT

Date: Season (Name It):   Days In This Season:

I Feel:

My Spirit Feels:

Today I Was Pushed To:

I Spent Time With God By:

Today I Felt That I Was Being Pulled
Away From:

Questions I Have:

This Season, I Am Seeing:

Answers To Questions The Spirit
Provided:

Today I Meditated On:

I Spent The Night Before:

Today I Noticed:

Last Night's Dream/Today's Daydream:

Today's Eureka Moment:

Last Night's Sleep Was _____.

IN
MY TIME ALONE, I AM
NOT
REALLY
ALONE.

MY DREAMS ARE MESSAGES FROM GOD.

CONNECTED NOTES

(Jot Down Your Thoughts Here)

HOLD ON, LET'S CONNECT

Date: Season (Name It):   Days In This Season:

I Feel: My Spirit Feels:

Today I Was Pushed To: I Spent Time With God By:

Today I Felt That I Was Being Pulled   Questions I Have:
Away From:

This Season, I Am Seeing: Answers To Questions The Spirit
                                           Provided:

Today I Meditated On:

                                           I Spent The Night Before:

Today I Noticed:

                                           Last Night's Dream/Today's Daydream:

Today's Eureka Moment:

Last Night's Sleep Was _____.

HOLD ON, LET'S CONNECT

Date: Season (Name It):   Days In This Season:

I Feel: My Spirit Feels:

Today I Was Pushed To: I Spent Time With God By:

Today I Felt That I Was Being Pulled   Questions I Have:
Away From:

This Season, I Am Seeing: Answers To Questions The Spirit
                                            Provided:

Today I Meditated On:

                                            I Spent The Night Before:

Today I Noticed:

                                            Last Night's Dream/Today's Daydream:

Today's Eureka Moment:

Last Night's Sleep Was _____.

HOLD ON, LET'S CONNECT

Date: Season (Name It):   Days In This Season:

I Feel: My Spirit Feels:

Today I Was Pushed To: I Spent Time With God By:

Today I Felt That I Was Being Pulled   Questions I Have:
Away From:

This Season, I Am Seeing: Answers To Questions The Spirit
                                              Provided:

Today I Meditated On:

                                              I Spent The Night Before:

Today I Noticed:

                                              Last Night's Dream/Today's Daydream:

Today's Eureka Moment:

Last Night's Sleep Was _____.

HOLD ON, LET'S CONNECT

Date: Season (Name It):   Days In This Season:

I Feel: My Spirit Feels:

Today I Was Pushed To: I Spent Time With God By:

Today I Felt That I Was Being Pulled   Questions I Have:
Away From:

This Season, I Am Seeing: Answers To Questions The Spirit
                                          Provided:

Today I Meditated On:

                                          I Spent The Night Before:

Today I Noticed:

                                          Last Night's Dream/Today's Daydream:

Today's Eureka Moment:

Last Night's Sleep Was _____.

I AM MORE
AWARE OF ...

HOLD ON, LET'S CONNECT

Date: Season (Name It):   Days In This Season:

I Feel: My Spirit Feels:

Today I Was Pushed To: I Spent Time With God By:

Today I Felt That I Was Being Pulled   Questions I Have:
Away From:

This Season, I Am Seeing: Answers To Questions The Spirit
                                                Provided:

Today I Meditated On:

                                                I Spent The Night Before:

Today I Noticed:

                                                Last Night's Dream/Today's Daydream:

Today's Eureka Moment:

Last Night's Sleep Was _____.

HOLD ON, LET'S CONNECT

Date: Season (Name It):   Days In This Season:

I Feel: My Spirit Feels:

Today I Was Pushed To: I Spent Time With God By:

Today I Felt That I Was Being Pulled   Questions I Have:
Away From:

This Season, I Am Seeing: Answers To Questions The Spirit
                                                 Provided:

Today I Meditated On:

                                                 I Spent The Night Before:

Today I Noticed:

                                                 Last Night's Dream/Today's Daydream:

Today's Eureka Moment:

Last Night's Sleep Was _____.

HOLD ON, LET'S CONNECT

Date: Season (Name It):   Days In This Season:

I Feel: My Spirit Feels:

Today I Was Pushed To: I Spent Time With God By:

Today I Felt That I Was Being Pulled   Questions I Have:
Away From:

This Season, I Am Seeing: Answers To Questions The Spirit
                                              Provided:

Today I Meditated On:

                                              I Spent The Night Before:

Today I Noticed:

                                              Last Night's Dream/Today's Daydream:

Today's Eureka Moment:

Last Night's Sleep Was _____.

CONNECTED NOTES

(Jot Down Your Thoughts Here)

HOLD ON, LET'S CONNECT

Date: Season (Name It):   Days In This Season:

I Feel: My Spirit Feels:

Today I Was Pushed To: I Spent Time With God By:

Today I Felt That I Was Being Pulled   Questions I Have:
Away From:

This Season, I Am Seeing: Answers To Questions The Spirit
                                              Provided:

Today I Meditated On:

                                              I Spent The Night Before:

Today I Noticed:

                                              Last Night's Dream/Today's Daydream:

Today's Eureka Moment:

Last Night's Sleep Was _____.

I AM
BLOSSOMING.
I AM
FLOURISHING.
I AM
BECOMING A BEAUTIFUL
BUTTERFLY.

DO NOT DISTURB. MY SPIRIT IS BEING FED.

HOLD ON, LET'S CONNECT

Date: Season (Name It):   Days In This Season:

I Feel:

My Spirit Feels:

Today I Was Pushed To:

I Spent Time With God By:

Today I Felt That I Was Being Pulled Away From:

Questions I Have:

This Season, I Am Seeing:

Answers To Questions The Spirit Provided:

Today I Meditated On:

I Spent The Night Before:

Today I Noticed:

Last Night's Dream/Today's Daydream:

Today's Eureka Moment:

Last Night's Sleep Was _____.

HOLD ON, LET'S CONNECT

Date: Season (Name It):   Days In This Season:

I Feel: My Spirit Feels:

Today I Was Pushed To: I Spent Time With God By:

Today I Felt That I Was Being Pulled   Questions I Have:
Away From:

This Season, I Am Seeing: Answers To Questions The Spirit
                                                 Provided:

Today I Meditated On:

                                                 I Spent The Night Before:

Today I Noticed:

                                                 Last Night's Dream/Today's Daydream:

Today's Eureka Moment:

Last Night's Sleep Was _____.

HOLD ON, LET'S CONNECT

Date: Season (Name It):   Days In This Season:

I Feel:

My Spirit Feels:

Today I Was Pushed To:

I Spent Time With God By:

Today I Felt That I Was Being Pulled
Away From:

Questions I Have:

This Season, I Am Seeing:

Answers To Questions The Spirit
Provided:

Today I Meditated On:

I Spent The Night Before:

Today I Noticed:

Last Night's Dream/Today's Daydream:

Today's Eureka Moment:

Last Night's Sleep Was _____.

HOLD ON, LET'S CONNECT

Date: Season (Name It):   Days In This Season:

I Feel: My Spirit Feels:

Today I Was Pushed To: I Spent Time With God By:

Today I Felt That I Was Being Pulled   Questions I Have:
Away From:

This Season, I Am Seeing: Answers To Questions The Spirit
                                                     Provided:

Today I Meditated On:

                                                     I Spent The Night Before:

Today I Noticed:

                                                     Last Night's Dream/Today's Daydream:

Today's Eureka Moment:

Last Night's Sleep Was _____.

CONNECTED NOTES

(Jot Down Your Thoughts Here)

HOLD ON, LET'S CONNECT

Date: Season (Name It):   Days In This Season:

I Feel: My Spirit Feels:

Today I Was Pushed To: I Spent Time With God By:

Today I Felt That I Was Being Pulled   Questions I Have:
Away From:

This Season, I Am Seeing: Answers To Questions The Spirit
                                             Provided:

Today I Meditated On:

                                             I Spent The Night Before:

Today I Noticed:

                                             Last Night's Dream/Today's Daydream:

Today's Eureka Moment:

Last Night's Sleep Was _____.

HOLD ON, LET'S CONNECT

Date: Season (Name It):   Days In This Season:

I Feel: My Spirit Feels:

Today I Was Pushed To: I Spent Time With God By:

Today I Felt That I Was Being Pulled   Questions I Have:
Away From:

This Season, I Am Seeing: Answers To Questions The Spirit
                                                     Provided:

Today I Meditated On:

                                                     I Spent The Night Before:

Today I Noticed:

                                                     Last Night's Dream/Today's Daydream:

Today's Eureka Moment:

Last Night's Sleep Was _____.

I BELIEVE GOD IS WORKING IN ME TO ...

HOLD ON, LET'S CONNECT

Date: Season (Name It):   Days In This Season:

I Feel: My Spirit Feels:

Today I Was Pushed To: I Spent Time With God By:

Today I Felt That I Was Being Pulled   Questions I Have:
Away From:

This Season, I Am Seeing: Answers To Questions The Spirit
                                                 Provided:

Today I Meditated On:

                                                 I Spent The Night Before:

Today I Noticed:

                                                 Last Night's Dream/Today's Daydream:

Today's Eureka Moment:

Last Night's Sleep Was _____.

HOLD ON, LET'S CONNECT

Date: Season (Name It):   Days In This Season:

I Feel: | My Spirit Feels:

Today I Was Pushed To: | I Spent Time With God By:

Today I Felt That I Was Being Pulled | Questions I Have:
Away From:

This Season, I Am Seeing: | Answers To Questions The Spirit
                                           | Provided:

Today I Meditated On:

                                           | I Spent The Night Before:

Today I Noticed:

                                           | Last Night's Dream/Today's Daydream:

Today's Eureka Moment:

Last Night's Sleep Was _____.

HOLD ON, LET'S CONNECT

Date: Season (Name It):   Days In This Season:

I Feel: My Spirit Feels:

Today I Was Pushed To: I Spent Time With God By:

Today I Felt That I Was Being Pulled   Questions I Have:
Away From:

This Season, I Am Seeing: Answers To Questions The Spirit
                                             Provided:

Today I Meditated On:

                                             I Spent The Night Before:

Today I Noticed:

                                             Last Night's Dream/Today's Daydream:

Today's Eureka Moment:

Last Night's Sleep Was _____.

THIS IS MY SEASON TO REAP WHAT I HAVE SOWN.

HOLD ON, LET'S CONNECT

Date: Season (Name It):   Days In This Season:

I Feel: My Spirit Feels:

Today I Was Pushed To: I Spent Time With God By:

Today I Felt That I Was Being Pulled   Questions I Have:
Away From:

This Season, I Am Seeing: Answers To Questions The Spirit
                                                Provided:

Today I Meditated On:

                                                I Spent The Night Before:

Today I Noticed:

                                                Last Night's Dream/Today's Daydream:

Today's Eureka Moment:

Last Night's Sleep Was _____.

HOLD ON, LET'S CONNECT

Date: Season (Name It):   Days In This Season:

I Feel: My Spirit Feels:

Today I Was Pushed To: I Spent Time With God By:

Today I Felt That I Was Being Pulled   Questions I Have:
Away From:

This Season, I Am Seeing: Answers To Questions The Spirit
                                                  Provided:

Today I Meditated On:

                                                  I Spent The Night Before:

Today I Noticed:

                                                  Last Night's Dream/Today's Daydream:

Today's Eureka Moment:

Last Night's Sleep Was _____.

HOLD ON, LET'S CONNECT

Date: Season (Name It):   Days In This Season:

I Feel: My Spirit Feels:

Today I Was Pushed To: I Spent Time With God By:

Today I Felt That I Was Being Pulled   Questions I Have:
Away From:

This Season, I Am Seeing: Answers To Questions The Spirit
                                           Provided:

Today I Meditated On:

                                           I Spent The Night Before:

Today I Noticed:

                                           Last Night's Dream/Today's Daydream:

Today's Eureka Moment:

Last Night's Sleep Was _____.

HOLD ON, LET'S CONNECT

Date: Season (Name It):   Days In This Season:

I Feel:

My Spirit Feels:

Today I Was Pushed To:

I Spent Time With God By:

Today I Felt That I Was Being Pulled
Away From:

Questions I Have:

This Season, I Am Seeing:

Answers To Questions The Spirit
Provided:

Today I Meditated On:

I Spent The Night Before:

Today I Noticed:

Last Night's Dream/Today's Daydream:

Today's Eureka Moment:

Last Night's Sleep Was _____.

I AM BEING TOLD TO KEEP QUIET AND PAY ATTENTION BECAUSE FAVOR IS BEING BESTOWED UPON ME.

I AM GETTING EVERYTHING I HAVE ASKED FOR. I CAN FEEL IT.

HOLD ON, LET'S CONNECT

Date: Season (Name It):   Days In This Season:

I Feel: My Spirit Feels:

Today I Was Pushed To: I Spent Time With God By:

Today I Felt That I Was Being Pulled   Questions I Have:
Away From:

This Season, I Am Seeing: Answers To Questions The Spirit
                                             Provided:

Today I Meditated On:

                                             I Spent The Night Before:

Today I Noticed:

                                             Last Night's Dream/Today's Daydream:

Today's Eureka Moment:

Last Night's Sleep Was _____.

HOLD ON, LET'S CONNECT

Date: Season (Name It):   Days In This Season:

I Feel: My Spirit Feels:

Today I Was Pushed To: I Spent Time With God By:

Today I Felt That I Was Being Pulled   Questions I Have:
Away From:

This Season, I Am Seeing: Answers To Questions The Spirit
                                                Provided:

Today I Meditated On:

                                                I Spent The Night Before:

Today I Noticed:

                                                Last Night's Dream/Today's Daydream:

Today's Eureka Moment:

Last Night's Sleep Was _____.

HOLD ON, LET'S CONNECT

Date: Season (Name It):   Days In This Season:

I Feel: My Spirit Feels:

Today I Was Pushed To: I Spent Time With God By:

Today I Felt That I Was Being Pulled   Questions I Have:
Away From:

This Season, I Am Seeing: Answers To Questions The Spirit
                                                Provided:

Today I Meditated On:

                                                I Spent The Night Before:

Today I Noticed:

                                                Last Night's Dream/Today's Daydream:

Today's Eureka Moment:

Last Night's Sleep Was _____.

CONNECTED NOTES

(Jot Down Your Thoughts Here)

I AM IN COMMUNION WITH ...

HOLD ON, LET'S CONNECT

Date: Season (Name It):   Days In This Season:

I Feel: My Spirit Feels:

Today I Was Pushed To: I Spent Time With God By:

Today I Felt That I Was Being Pulled   Questions I Have:
Away From:

This Season, I Am Seeing: Answers To Questions The Spirit
                                                Provided:

Today I Meditated On:

                                                I Spent The Night Before:

Today I Noticed:

                                                Last Night's Dream/Today's Daydream:

Today's Eureka Moment:

Last Night's Sleep Was _____.

HOLD ON, LET'S CONNECT

Date: Season (Name It):   Days In This Season:

I Feel: My Spirit Feels:

Today I Was Pushed To: I Spent Time With God By:

Today I Felt That I Was Being Pulled   Questions I Have:
Away From:

This Season, I Am Seeing: Answers To Questions The Spirit
                                                  Provided:

Today I Meditated On:

                                                  I Spent The Night Before:

Today I Noticed:

                                                  Last Night's Dream/Today's Daydream:

Today's Eureka Moment:

Last Night's Sleep Was _____.

HOLD ON, LET'S CONNECT

Date: Season (Name It):   Days In This Season:

I Feel: My Spirit Feels:

Today I Was Pushed To: I Spent Time With God By:

Today I Felt That I Was Being Pulled   Questions I Have:
Away From:

This Season, I Am Seeing: Answers To Questions The Spirit
                                                      Provided:

Today I Meditated On:

                                                      I Spent The Night Before:

Today I Noticed:

                                                      Last Night's Dream/Today's Daydream:

Today's Eureka Moment:

Last Night's Sleep Was _____.

CONNECTED NOTES

(Jot Down Your Thoughts Here)

HOLD ON, LET'S CONNECT

Date: Season (Name It):   Days In This Season:

I Feel: My Spirit Feels:

Today I Was Pushed To: I Spent Time With God By:

Today I Felt That I Was Being Pulled   Questions I Have:
Away From:

This Season, I Am Seeing: Answers To Questions The Spirit
                                           Provided:

Today I Meditated On:
                                           I Spent The Night Before:

Today I Noticed:
                                           Last Night's Dream/Today's Daydream:

Today's Eureka Moment:

Last Night's Sleep Was _____.

HOLD ON, LET'S CONNECT

Date: Season (Name It):   Days In This Season:

I Feel: My Spirit Feels:

Today I Was Pushed To: I Spent Time With God By:

Today I Felt That I Was Being Pulled   Questions I Have:
Away From:

This Season, I Am Seeing: Answers To Questions The Spirit
                                             Provided:

Today I Meditated On:

                                             I Spent The Night Before:

Today I Noticed:

                                             Last Night's Dream/Today's Daydream:

Today's Eureka Moment:

Last Night's Sleep Was _____.

HOLD ON, LET'S CONNECT

Date: Season (Name It):   Days In This Season:

I Feel: My Spirit Feels:

Today I Was Pushed To: I Spent Time With God By:

Today I Felt That I Was Being Pulled   Questions I Have:
Away From:

This Season, I Am Seeing: Answers To Questions The Spirit
                                                Provided:

Today I Meditated On:

                                                I Spent The Night Before:

Today I Noticed:

                                                Last Night's Dream/Today's Daydream:

Today's Eureka Moment:

Last Night's Sleep Was _____.

HOLD ON, LET'S CONNECT

Date: Season (Name It):   Days In This Season:

I Feel: | My Spirit Feels:

Today I Was Pushed To: | I Spent Time With God By:

Today I Felt That I Was Being Pulled | Questions I Have:
Away From:

This Season, I Am Seeing: | Answers To Questions The Spirit
                                             | Provided:

Today I Meditated On:

                                             | I Spent The Night Before:

Today I Noticed:

                                             | Last Night's Dream/Today's Daydream:

Today's Eureka Moment:

Last Night's Sleep Was _____.

I AM BEING ELEVATED. THINGS ARE WORKING IN MY FAVOR.

HOLD ON, LET'S CONNECT

Date: Season (Name It):   Days In This Season:

I Feel: My Spirit Feels:

Today I Was Pushed To: I Spent Time With God By:

Today I Felt That I Was Being Pulled   Questions I Have:
Away From:

This Season, I Am Seeing: Answers To Questions The Spirit
                                                 Provided:

Today I Meditated On:

                                                 I Spent The Night Before:

Today I Noticed:

                                                 Last Night's Dream/Today's Daydream:

Today's Eureka Moment:

Last Night's Sleep Was _____.

HOLD ON, LET'S CONNECT

Date: Season (Name It):   Days In This Season:

I Feel: My Spirit Feels:

Today I Was Pushed To: I Spent Time With God By:

Today I Felt That I Was Being Pulled   Questions I Have:
Away From:

This Season, I Am Seeing: Answers To Questions The Spirit
                                           Provided:

Today I Meditated On:

                                           I Spent The Night Before:

Today I Noticed:

                                           Last Night's Dream/Today's Daydream:

Today's Eureka Moment:

Last Night's Sleep Was _____.

CONNECTED NOTES

(Jot Down Your Thoughts Here)

HOLD ON, LET'S CONNECT

Date: Season (Name It):   Days In This Season:

I Feel: My Spirit Feels:

Today I Was Pushed To: I Spent Time With God By:

Today I Felt That I Was Being Pulled   Questions I Have:
Away From:

This Season, I Am Seeing: Answers To Questions The Spirit
                                                        Provided:

Today I Meditated On:

                                                        I Spent The Night Before:

Today I Noticed:

                                                        Last Night's Dream/Today's Daydream:

Today's Eureka Moment:

Last Night's Sleep Was _____.

HOLD ON, LET'S CONNECT

Date: Season (Name It):   Days In This Season:

I Feel: My Spirit Feels:

Today I Was Pushed To: I Spent Time With God By:

Today I Felt That I Was Being Pulled   Questions I Have:
Away From:

This Season, I Am Seeing: Answers To Questions The Spirit
                                           Provided:

Today I Meditated On:

                                           I Spent The Night Before:

Today I Noticed:

                                           Last Night's Dream/Today's Daydream:

Today's Eureka Moment:

Last Night's Sleep Was _____.

I AM QUIET BECAUSE SOMETHING IS BEING SAID TO ME THAT OTHERS CAN'T HEAR.

I AM IN

LOVE WITH WHAT

BELONGS TO ME.

HOLD ON, LET'S CONNECT

Date: Season (Name It):   Days In This Season:

I Feel: My Spirit Feels:

Today I Was Pushed To: I Spent Time With God By:

Today I Felt That I Was Being Pulled   Questions I Have:
Away From:

This Season, I Am Seeing: Answers To Questions The Spirit
                                           Provided:

Today I Meditated On:

                                           I Spent The Night Before:

Today I Noticed:

                                           Last Night's Dream/Today's Daydream:

Today's Eureka Moment:

Last Night's Sleep Was _____.

HOLD ON, LET'S CONNECT

Date: Season (Name It):   Days In This Season:

I Feel: My Spirit Feels:

Today I Was Pushed To: I Spent Time With God By:

Today I Felt That I Was Being Pulled   Questions I Have:
Away From:

This Season, I Am Seeing: Answers To Questions The Spirit
                                       Provided:

Today I Meditated On:

                                       I Spent The Night Before:

Today I Noticed:

                                       Last Night's Dream/Today's Daydream:

Today's Eureka Moment:

Last Night's Sleep Was _____.

HOLD ON, LET'S CONNECT

Date: Season (Name It):   Days In This Season:

I Feel: My Spirit Feels:

Today I Was Pushed To: I Spent Time With God By:

Today I Felt That I Was Being Pulled   Questions I Have:
Away From:

This Season, I Am Seeing: Answers To Questions The Spirit
                                                       Provided:

Today I Meditated On:

                                                       I Spent The Night Before:

Today I Noticed:

                                                       Last Night's Dream/Today's Daydream:

Today's Eureka Moment:

Last Night's Sleep Was _____.

CONNECTED NOTES

(Jot Down Your Thoughts Here)

MY SPIRIT SHOWED IT TO ME

BEFORE IT ACTUALLY MANIFESTED

ITSELF.

HOLD ON, LET'S CONNECT

Date: Season (Name It):   Days In This Season:

I Feel: | My Spirit Feels:

Today I Was Pushed To: | I Spent Time With God By:

Today I Felt That I Was Being Pulled | Questions I Have:
Away From:

This Season, I Am Seeing: | Answers To Questions The Spirit
                                                     | Provided:

Today I Meditated On: |
                                                     | I Spent The Night Before:

Today I Noticed: |
                                                     | Last Night's Dream/Today's Daydream:

Today's Eureka Moment: |

Last Night's Sleep Was _____.

HOLD ON, LET'S CONNECT

Date: Season (Name It):   Days In This Season:

I Feel: My Spirit Feels:

Today I Was Pushed To: I Spent Time With God By:

Today I Felt That I Was Being Pulled   Questions I Have:
Away From:

This Season, I Am Seeing: Answers To Questions The Spirit
                                           Provided:

Today I Meditated On:

                                           I Spent The Night Before:

Today I Noticed:

                                           Last Night's Dream/Today's Daydream:

Today's Eureka Moment:

Last Night's Sleep Was _____.

SOME THINGS
ARE BEING PULLED
AWAY
FROM ME AND
SOME THINGS
ARE BEING PULLED
TOWARDS
ME.
I AM OKAY WITH BOTH.

I DON'T RESIST. I FLOW.

HOLD ON, LET'S CONNECT

Date: Season (Name It):   Days In This Season:

I Feel: My Spirit Feels:

Today I Was Pushed To: I Spent Time With God By:

Today I Felt That I Was Being Pulled   Questions I Have:
Away From:

This Season, I Am Seeing: Answers To Questions The Spirit
                                                 Provided:

Today I Meditated On:

                                                 I Spent The Night Before:

Today I Noticed:

                                                 Last Night's Dream/Today's Daydream:

Today's Eureka Moment:

Last Night's Sleep Was _____.

HOLD ON, LET'S CONNECT

Date: Season (Name It):   Days In This Season:

I Feel: | My Spirit Feels:

Today I Was Pushed To: | I Spent Time With God By:

Today I Felt That I Was Being Pulled | Questions I Have:
Away From:

This Season, I Am Seeing: | Answers To Questions The Spirit
                                           | Provided:

Today I Meditated On:

                                           | I Spent The Night Before:

Today I Noticed:

                                           | Last Night's Dream/Today's Daydream:

Today's Eureka Moment:

Last Night's Sleep Was _____.

HOLD ON, LET'S CONNECT

Date: Season (Name It):   Days In This Season:

I Feel: My Spirit Feels:

Today I Was Pushed To: I Spent Time With God By:

Today I Felt That I Was Being Pulled   Questions I Have:
Away From:

This Season, I Am Seeing: Answers To Questions The Spirit
                                                Provided:

Today I Meditated On:

                                                I Spent The Night Before:

Today I Noticed:

                                                Last Night's Dream/Today's Daydream:

Today's Eureka Moment:

Last Night's Sleep Was _____.

HOLD ON, LET'S CONNECT

Date: Season (Name It):   Days In This Season:

I Feel: My Spirit Feels:

Today I Was Pushed To: I Spent Time With God By:

Today I Felt That I Was Being Pulled   Questions I Have:
Away From:

This Season, I Am Seeing: Answers To Questions The Spirit
                                                 Provided:

Today I Meditated On:

                                                 I Spent The Night Before:

Today I Noticed:

                                                 Last Night's Dream/Today's Daydream:

Today's Eureka Moment:

Last Night's Sleep Was _____.

CONNECTED NOTES

(Jot Down Your Thoughts Here)

I NOW VIEW
GOD AS ...

HOLD ON, LET'S CONNECT

Date: Season (Name It):   Days In This Season:

I Feel: My Spirit Feels:

Today I Was Pushed To: I Spent Time With God By:

Today I Felt That I Was Being Pulled   Questions I Have:
Away From:

This Season, I Am Seeing: Answers To Questions The Spirit
                                           Provided:

Today I Meditated On:

                                           I Spent The Night Before:

Today I Noticed:

                                           Last Night's Dream/Today's Daydream:

Today's Eureka Moment:

Last Night's Sleep Was _____.

HOLD ON, LET'S CONNECT

Date: Season (Name It):   Days In This Season:

I Feel: My Spirit Feels:

Today I Was Pushed To: I Spent Time With God By:

Today I Felt That I Was Being Pulled   Questions I Have:
Away From:

This Season, I Am Seeing: Answers To Questions The Spirit
                                                 Provided:

Today I Meditated On:

                                                 I Spent The Night Before:

Today I Noticed:

                                                 Last Night's Dream/Today's Daydream:

Today's Eureka Moment:

Last Night's Sleep Was _____.

SPEAK LIFE.

I HAVE THE PATIENCE TO WATCH WHAT I DON'T UNDERSTAND UNFOLD.

HOLD ON, LET'S CONNECT

Date: Season (Name It):   Days In This Season:

I Feel: My Spirit Feels:

Today I Was Pushed To: I Spent Time With God By:

Today I Felt That I Was Being Pulled   Questions I Have:
Away From:

This Season, I Am Seeing: Answers To Questions The Spirit
                                       Provided:

Today I Meditated On:

                                       I Spent The Night Before:

Today I Noticed:

                                       Last Night's Dream/Today's Daydream:

Today's Eureka Moment:

Last Night's Sleep Was _____.

HOLD ON, LET'S CONNECT

Date: Season (Name It):   Days In This Season:

I Feel: My Spirit Feels:

Today I Was Pushed To: I Spent Time With God By:

Today I Felt That I Was Being Pulled   Questions I Have:
Away From:

This Season, I Am Seeing: Answers To Questions The Spirit
                                           Provided:

Today I Meditated On:

                                           I Spent The Night Before:

Today I Noticed:

                                           Last Night's Dream/Today's Daydream:

Today's Eureka Moment:

Last Night's Sleep Was _____.

HOLD ON, LET'S CONNECT

Date: Season (Name It):   Days In This Season:

I Feel: My Spirit Feels:

Today I Was Pushed To: I Spent Time With God By:

Today I Felt That I Was Being Pulled   Questions I Have:
Away From:

This Season, I Am Seeing: Answers To Questions The Spirit
                                           Provided:

Today I Meditated On:

                                           I Spent The Night Before:

Today I Noticed:

                                           Last Night's Dream/Today's Daydream:

Today's Eureka Moment:

Last Night's Sleep Was _____.

HOLD ON, LET'S CONNECT

Date: Season (Name It):   Days In This Season:

I Feel: My Spirit Feels:

Today I Was Pushed To: I Spent Time With God By:

Today I Felt That I Was Being Pulled   Questions I Have:
Away From:

This Season, I Am Seeing: Answers To Questions The Spirit
                                                      Provided:

Today I Meditated On:

                                                      I Spent The Night Before:

Today I Noticed:

                                                      Last Night's Dream/Today's Daydream:

Today's Eureka Moment:

Last Night's Sleep Was _____.

HOLD ON, LET'S CONNECT

Date: Season (Name It):   Days In This Season:

I Feel: My Spirit Feels:

Today I Was Pushed To: I Spent Time With God By:

Today I Felt That I Was Being Pulled   Questions I Have:
Away From:

This Season, I Am Seeing: Answers To Questions The Spirit
                                           Provided:

Today I Meditated On:

                                           I Spent The Night Before:

Today I Noticed:

                                           Last Night's Dream/Today's Daydream:

Today's Eureka Moment:

Last Night's Sleep Was _____.

CONNECTED NOTES

(Jot Down Your Thoughts Here)

I SUDDENLY HAVE THE URGE TO ...

HOLD ON, LET'S CONNECT

Date: Season (Name It):   Days In This Season:

I Feel: My Spirit Feels:

Today I Was Pushed To: I Spent Time With God By:

Today I Felt That I Was Being Pulled   Questions I Have:
Away From:

This Season, I Am Seeing: Answers To Questions The Spirit
                                           Provided:

Today I Meditated On:

                                           I Spent The Night Before:

Today I Noticed:

                                           Last Night's Dream/Today's Daydream:

Today's Eureka Moment:

Last Night's Sleep Was _____.

HOLD ON, LET'S CONNECT

Date: Season (Name It):   Days In This Season:

I Feel:	My Spirit Feels:
Today I Was Pushed To:	I Spent Time With God By:
Today I Felt That I Was Being Pulled Away From:	Questions I Have:
This Season, I Am Seeing:	Answers To Questions The Spirit Provided:
Today I Meditated On:	I Spent The Night Before:
Today I Noticed:	Last Night's Dream/Today's Daydream:
Today's Eureka Moment:	

Last Night's Sleep Was _____.

HOLD ON, LET'S CONNECT

Date: Season (Name It):   Days In This Season:

I Feel: My Spirit Feels:

Today I Was Pushed To: I Spent Time With God By:

Today I Felt That I Was Being Pulled   Questions I Have:
Away From:

This Season, I Am Seeing: Answers To Questions The Spirit
                                       Provided:

Today I Meditated On:

                                       I Spent The Night Before:

Today I Noticed:

                                       Last Night's Dream/Today's Daydream:

Today's Eureka Moment:

Last Night's Sleep Was _____.

HOLD ON, LET'S CONNECT

Date: Season (Name It):   Days In This Season:

I Feel: My Spirit Feels:

Today I Was Pushed To: I Spent Time With God By:

Today I Felt That I Was Being Pulled   Questions I Have:
Away From:

This Season, I Am Seeing: Answers To Questions The Spirit
                                                Provided:

Today I Meditated On:

                                                I Spent The Night Before:

Today I Noticed:

                                                Last Night's Dream/Today's Daydream:

Today's Eureka Moment:

Last Night's Sleep Was _____.

CONNECTED NOTES

(Jot Down Your Thoughts Here)

I LOVE WATCHING MY WORDS MANIFEST THEMSELVES.

I MUST
SPIRITUALLY FEEL
IT
BEFORE I CAN
PHYSICALLY
SEE IT.

HOLD ON, LET'S CONNECT

Date: Season (Name It):   Days In This Season:

I Feel: | My Spirit Feels:

Today I Was Pushed To: | I Spent Time With God By:

Today I Felt That I Was Being Pulled | Questions I Have:
Away From:

This Season, I Am Seeing: | Answers To Questions The Spirit
                                           | Provided:

Today I Meditated On:
                                           | I Spent The Night Before:

Today I Noticed:
                                           | Last Night's Dream/Today's Daydream:

Today's Eureka Moment:

Last Night's Sleep Was _____.

HOLD ON, LET'S CONNECT

Date: Season (Name It):   Days In This Season:

I Feel: My Spirit Feels:

Today I Was Pushed To: I Spent Time With God By:

Today I Felt That I Was Being Pulled   Questions I Have:
Away From:

This Season, I Am Seeing: Answers To Questions The Spirit
                                           Provided:

Today I Meditated On:

                                           I Spent The Night Before:

Today I Noticed:

                                           Last Night's Dream/Today's Daydream:

Today's Eureka Moment:

Last Night's Sleep Was _____.

HOLD ON, LET'S CONNECT

Date: Season (Name It):   Days In This Season:

I Feel: My Spirit Feels:

Today I Was Pushed To: I Spent Time With God By:

Today I Felt That I Was Being Pulled   Questions I Have:
Away From:

This Season, I Am Seeing: Answers To Questions The Spirit
                                                     Provided:

Today I Meditated On:

                                                     I Spent The Night Before:

Today I Noticed:

                                                     Last Night's Dream/Today's Daydream:

Today's Eureka Moment:

Last Night's Sleep Was _____.

HOLD ON, LET'S CONNECT

Date: Season (Name It):   Days In This Season:

I Feel: My Spirit Feels:

Today I Was Pushed To: I Spent Time With God By:

Today I Felt That I Was Being Pulled   Questions I Have:
Away From:

This Season, I Am Seeing: Answers To Questions The Spirit
                                           Provided:

Today I Meditated On:

                                           I Spent The Night Before:

Today I Noticed:

                                           Last Night's Dream/Today's Daydream:

Today's Eureka Moment:

Last Night's Sleep Was _____.

HOLD ON, LET'S CONNECT

Date: Season (Name It):   Days In This Season:

I Feel: My Spirit Feels:

Today I Was Pushed To: I Spent Time With God By:

Today I Felt That I Was Being Pulled   Questions I Have:
Away From:

This Season, I Am Seeing: Answers To Questions The Spirit
                                           Provided:

Today I Meditated On:

                                           I Spent The Night Before:

Today I Noticed:

                                           Last Night's Dream/Today's Daydream:

Today's Eureka Moment:

Last Night's Sleep Was _____.

I AM NOTICING THESE THINGS TRANSFORM ...

MY SPIRIT IS YEARNING FOR ...

HOLD ON, LET'S CONNECT

Date: Season (Name It):   Days In This Season:

I Feel: | My Spirit Feels:

Today I Was Pushed To: | I Spent Time With God By:

Today I Felt That I Was Being Pulled | Questions I Have:
Away From:

This Season, I Am Seeing: | Answers To Questions The Spirit
                                                 | Provided:

Today I Meditated On:

                                                 | I Spent The Night Before:

Today I Noticed:

                                                 | Last Night's Dream/Today's Daydream:

Today's Eureka Moment:

Last Night's Sleep Was _____.

HOLD ON, LET'S CONNECT

Date: Season (Name It):   Days In This Season:

I Feel: My Spirit Feels:

Today I Was Pushed To: I Spent Time With God By:

Today I Felt That I Was Being Pulled   Questions I Have:
Away From:

This Season, I Am Seeing: Answers To Questions The Spirit
                                                  Provided:

Today I Meditated On:

                                                  I Spent The Night Before:

Today I Noticed:

                                                  Last Night's Dream/Today's Daydream:

Today's Eureka Moment:

Last Night's Sleep Was _____.

HOLD ON, LET'S CONNECT

Date: Season (Name It):   Days In This Season:

I Feel: My Spirit Feels:

Today I Was Pushed To: I Spent Time With God By:

Today I Felt That I Was Being Pulled   Questions I Have:
Away From:

This Season, I Am Seeing: Answers To Questions The Spirit
                                                  Provided:

Today I Meditated On:

                                                  I Spent The Night Before:

Today I Noticed:

                                                  Last Night's Dream/Today's Daydream:

Today's Eureka Moment:

Last Night's Sleep Was _____.

CONNECTED NOTES

(Jot Down Your Thoughts Here)

HOLD ON, LET'S CONNECT

Date: Season (Name It):   Days In This Season:

I Feel: My Spirit Feels:

Today I Was Pushed To: I Spent Time With God By:

Today I Felt That I Was Being Pulled   Questions I Have:
Away From:

This Season, I Am Seeing: Answers To Questions The Spirit
                                                 Provided:

Today I Meditated On:

                                                 I Spent The Night Before:

Today I Noticed:

                                                 Last Night's Dream/Today's Daydream:

Today's Eureka Moment:

Last Night's Sleep Was _____.

HOLD ON, LET'S CONNECT

Date: Season (Name It):   Days In This Season:

I Feel: My Spirit Feels:

Today I Was Pushed To: I Spent Time With God By:

Today I Felt That I Was Being Pulled   Questions I Have:
Away From:

This Season, I Am Seeing: Answers To Questions The Spirit
                                                 Provided:

Today I Meditated On:

                                                 I Spent The Night Before:

Today I Noticed:

                                                 Last Night's Dream/Today's Daydream:

Today's Eureka Moment:

Last Night's Sleep Was _____.

HOLD ON, LET'S CONNECT

Date: Season (Name It):   Days In This Season:

I Feel: My Spirit Feels:

Today I Was Pushed To: I Spent Time With God By:

Today I Felt That I Was Being Pulled   Questions I Have:
Away From:

This Season, I Am Seeing: Answers To Questions The Spirit
                                           Provided:

Today I Meditated On:

                                           I Spent The Night Before:

Today I Noticed:

                                           Last Night's Dream/Today's Daydream:

Today's Eureka Moment:

Last Night's Sleep Was _____.

TODAY
IS THE BIRTH OF
SOMETHING
NEW.
I AM RENEWED
IN THE MIND
AND
SPIRIT.

TODAY
I AM SHEDDING MY
OLD
THOUGHTS
AND
FEELINGS FOR NATURAL FEELINGS OF
LOVE
AND ENCOURAGEMENT.

HOLD ON, LET'S CONNECT

Date: Season (Name It):   Days In This Season:

I Feel: My Spirit Feels:

Today I Was Pushed To: I Spent Time With God By:

Today I Felt That I Was Being Pulled   Questions I Have:
Away From:

This Season, I Am Seeing: Answers To Questions The Spirit
                                                 Provided:

Today I Meditated On:

                                                 I Spent The Night Before:

Today I Noticed:

                                                 Last Night's Dream/Today's Daydream:

Today's Eureka Moment:

Last Night's Sleep Was _____.

HOLD ON, LET'S CONNECT

Date: Season (Name It):   Days In This Season:

I Feel: | My Spirit Feels:

Today I Was Pushed To: | I Spent Time With God By:

Today I Felt That I Was Being Pulled | Questions I Have:
Away From:

This Season, I Am Seeing: | Answers To Questions The Spirit
                                                | Provided:

Today I Meditated On:

                                                | I Spent The Night Before:

Today I Noticed:

                                                | Last Night's Dream/Today's Daydream:

Today's Eureka Moment:

Last Night's Sleep Was _____.

HOLD ON, LET'S CONNECT

Date: Season (Name It):   Days In This Season:

I Feel: My Spirit Feels:

Today I Was Pushed To: I Spent Time With God By:

Today I Felt That I Was Being Pulled   Questions I Have:
Away From:

This Season, I Am Seeing: Answers To Questions The Spirit
                                                Provided:

Today I Meditated On:

                                                I Spent The Night Before:

Today I Noticed:

                                                Last Night's Dream/Today's Daydream:

Today's Eureka Moment:

Last Night's Sleep Was _____.

I AM
IN AMAZEMENT
THAT
WHAT
I PRAYED FOR HAS
HAPPENED TO
ME.

I FEEL SAFE WHEN I ...

HOLD ON, LET'S CONNECT

Date: Season (Name It):   Days In This Season:

I Feel: My Spirit Feels:

Today I Was Pushed To: I Spent Time With God By:

Today I Felt That I Was Being Pulled   Questions I Have:
Away From:

This Season, I Am Seeing: Answers To Questions The Spirit
                                           Provided:

Today I Meditated On:

                                           I Spent The Night Before:

Today I Noticed:

                                           Last Night's Dream/Today's Daydream:

Today's Eureka Moment:

Last Night's Sleep Was _____.

HOLD ON, LET'S CONNECT

Date: Season (Name It):   Days In This Season:

I Feel: My Spirit Feels:

Today I Was Pushed To: I Spent Time With God By:

Today I Felt That I Was Being Pulled   Questions I Have:
Away From:

This Season, I Am Seeing: Answers To Questions The Spirit
                                             Provided:

Today I Meditated On:

                                             I Spent The Night Before:

Today I Noticed:

                                             Last Night's Dream/Today's Daydream:

Today's Eureka Moment:

Last Night's Sleep Was _____.

HOLD ON, LET'S CONNECT

Date: Season (Name It):   Days In This Season:

I Feel: My Spirit Feels:

Today I Was Pushed To: I Spent Time With God By:

Today I Felt That I Was Being Pulled   Questions I Have:
Away From:

This Season, I Am Seeing: Answers To Questions The Spirit
                                                 Provided:

Today I Meditated On:

                                                 I Spent The Night Before:

Today I Noticed:

                                                 Last Night's Dream/Today's Daydream:

Today's Eureka Moment:

Last Night's Sleep Was _____.

HOLD ON, LET'S CONNECT

Date: Season (Name It):   Days In This Season:

I Feel: My Spirit Feels:

Today I Was Pushed To: I Spent Time With God By:

Today I Felt That I Was Being Pulled   Questions I Have:
Away From:

This Season, I Am Seeing: Answers To Questions The Spirit
                                                    Provided:

Today I Meditated On:

                                                    I Spent The Night Before:

Today I Noticed:

                                                    Last Night's Dream/Today's Daydream:

Today's Eureka Moment:

Last Night's Sleep Was _____.

IN
THIS CURRENT SEASON,
I AM
IN OBSERVATION
MODE.

HOLD ON, LET'S CONNECT

Date: Season (Name It):   Days In This Season:

I Feel: My Spirit Feels:

Today I Was Pushed To: I Spent Time With God By:

Today I Felt That I Was Being Pulled   Questions I Have:
Away From:

This Season, I Am Seeing: Answers To Questions The Spirit
                                           Provided:

Today I Meditated On:

                                           I Spent The Night Before:

Today I Noticed:

                                           Last Night's Dream/Today's Daydream:

Today's Eureka Moment:

Last Night's Sleep Was _____.

HOLD ON, LET'S CONNECT

Date: Season (Name It):   Days In This Season:

I Feel:

My Spirit Feels:

Today I Was Pushed To:

I Spent Time With God By:

Today I Felt That I Was Being Pulled Away From:

Questions I Have:

This Season, I Am Seeing:

Answers To Questions The Spirit Provided:

Today I Meditated On:

I Spent The Night Before:

Today I Noticed:

Last Night's Dream/Today's Daydream:

Today's Eureka Moment:

Last Night's Sleep Was _____.

HOLD ON, LET'S CONNECT

Date: Season (Name It):   Days In This Season:

I Feel: My Spirit Feels:

Today I Was Pushed To: I Spent Time With God By:

Today I Felt That I Was Being Pulled   Questions I Have:
Away From:

This Season, I Am Seeing: Answers To Questions The Spirit
                                       Provided:

Today I Meditated On:

                                       I Spent The Night Before:

Today I Noticed:

                                       Last Night's Dream/Today's Daydream:

Today's Eureka Moment:

Last Night's Sleep Was _____.

CONNECTED NOTES

(Jot Down Your Thoughts Here)

HOLD ON, LET'S CONNECT

Date: Season (Name It):   Days In This Season:

I Feel:	My Spirit Feels:
Today I Was Pushed To:	I Spent Time With God By:
Today I Felt That I Was Being Pulled Away From:	Questions I Have:
This Season, I Am Seeing:	Answers To Questions The Spirit Provided:
Today I Meditated On:	
	I Spent The Night Before:
Today I Noticed:	
	Last Night's Dream/Today's Daydream:
Today's Eureka Moment:	

Last Night's Sleep Was _____.

HOLD ON, LET'S CONNECT

Date: Season (Name It):   Days In This Season:

I Feel:

My Spirit Feels:

Today I Was Pushed To:

I Spent Time With God By:

Today I Felt That I Was Being Pulled Away From:

Questions I Have:

This Season, I Am Seeing:

Answers To Questions The Spirit Provided:

Today I Meditated On:

I Spent The Night Before:

Today I Noticed:

Last Night's Dream/Today's Daydream:

Today's Eureka Moment:

Last Night's Sleep Was _____.

HOLD ON, LET'S CONNECT

Date: Season (Name It):   Days In This Season:

I Feel: My Spirit Feels:

Today I Was Pushed To: I Spent Time With God By:

Today I Felt That I Was Being Pulled   Questions I Have:
Away From:

This Season, I Am Seeing: Answers To Questions The Spirit
                                           Provided:

Today I Meditated On:

                                           I Spent The Night Before:

Today I Noticed:

                                           Last Night's Dream/Today's Daydream:

Today's Eureka Moment:

Last Night's Sleep Was _____.

THIS
UNEXPLAINABLE
FEELING IS THE
RESULT
OF A MIRACLE
THAT HAS JUST
BEEN
BIRTHED.

HOLD ON, LET'S CONNECT

Date: Season (Name It):   Days In This Season:

I Feel: My Spirit Feels:

Today I Was Pushed To: I Spent Time With God By:

Today I Felt That I Was Being Pulled   Questions I Have:
Away From:

This Season, I Am Seeing: Answers To Questions The Spirit
                                                     Provided:

Today I Meditated On:

                                                     I Spent The Night Before:

Today I Noticed:

                                                     Last Night's Dream/Today's Daydream:

Today's Eureka Moment:

Last Night's Sleep Was _____.

HOLD ON, LET'S CONNECT

Date: Season (Name It):   Days In This Season:

I Feel: | My Spirit Feels:

Today I Was Pushed To: | I Spent Time With God By:

Today I Felt That I Was Being Pulled | Questions I Have:
Away From:

This Season, I Am Seeing: | Answers To Questions The Spirit
                                             | Provided:

Today I Meditated On:

                                             | I Spent The Night Before:

Today I Noticed:

                                             | Last Night's Dream/Today's Daydream:

Today's Eureka Moment:

Last Night's Sleep Was _____.

HOLD ON, LET'S CONNECT

Date: Season (Name It):   Days In This Season:

I Feel: My Spirit Feels:

Today I Was Pushed To: I Spent Time With God By:

Today I Felt That I Was Being Pulled   Questions I Have:
Away From:

This Season, I Am Seeing: Answers To Questions The Spirit
                                                       Provided:

Today I Meditated On:

                                                       I Spent The Night Before:

Today I Noticed:

                                                       Last Night's Dream/Today's Daydream:

Today's Eureka Moment:

Last Night's Sleep Was _____.

HOLD ON, LET'S CONNECT

Date: Season (Name It):   Days In This Season:

I Feel: My Spirit Feels:

Today I Was Pushed To: I Spent Time With God By:

Today I Felt That I Was Being Pulled   Questions I Have:
Away From:

This Season, I Am Seeing: Answers To Questions The Spirit
                                                     Provided:

Today I Meditated On:

                                                     I Spent The Night Before:

Today I Noticed:

                                                     Last Night's Dream/Today's Daydream:

Today's Eureka Moment:

Last Night's Sleep Was _____.

HOLD ON, LET'S CONNECT

Date: Season (Name It):   Days In This Season:

I Feel: My Spirit Feels:

Today I Was Pushed To: I Spent Time With God By:

Today I Felt That I Was Being Pulled   Questions I Have:
Away From:

This Season, I Am Seeing: Answers To Questions The Spirit
                                                  Provided:

Today I Meditated On:

                                                  I Spent The Night Before:

Today I Noticed:

                                                  Last Night's Dream/Today's Daydream:

Today's Eureka Moment:

Last Night's Sleep Was _____.

HOLD ON, LET'S CONNECT

Date: Season (Name It):   Days In This Season:

I Feel: My Spirit Feels:

Today I Was Pushed To: I Spent Time With God By:

Today I Felt That I Was Being Pulled   Questions I Have:
Away From:

This Season, I Am Seeing: Answers To Questions The Spirit
                                                  Provided:

Today I Meditated On:

                                                  I Spent The Night Before:

Today I Noticed:

                                                  Last Night's Dream/Today's Daydream:

Today's Eureka Moment:

Last Night's Sleep Was _____.

PRAYER LIFE FOR ME FEELS LIKE ...

WHAT
IS BEING
REQUIRED OF
ME
IS SOMETHING THAT I
MUST
KEEP TO MYSELF.

HOLD ON, LET'S CONNECT

Date: Season (Name It):   Days In This Season:

I Feel: My Spirit Feels:

Today I Was Pushed To: I Spent Time With God By:

Today I Felt That I Was Being Pulled   Questions I Have:
Away From:

This Season, I Am Seeing: Answers To Questions The Spirit
                                                  Provided:

Today I Meditated On:

                                                  I Spent The Night Before:

Today I Noticed:

                                                  Last Night's Dream/Today's Daydream:

Today's Eureka Moment:

Last Night's Sleep Was _____.

HOLD ON, LET'S CONNECT

Date: Season (Name It):   Days In This Season:

I Feel: My Spirit Feels:

Today I Was Pushed To: I Spent Time With God By:

Today I Felt That I Was Being Pulled   Questions I Have:
Away From:

This Season, I Am Seeing: Answers To Questions The Spirit
                                                         Provided:

Today I Meditated On:

                                                         I Spent The Night Before:

Today I Noticed:

                                                         Last Night's Dream/Today's Daydream:

Today's Eureka Moment:

Last Night's Sleep Was _____.

HOLD ON, LET'S CONNECT

Date: Season (Name It):   Days In This Season:

I Feel: My Spirit Feels:

Today I Was Pushed To: I Spent Time With God By:

Today I Felt That I Was Being Pulled   Questions I Have:
Away From:

This Season, I Am Seeing: Answers To Questions The Spirit
                                               Provided:

Today I Meditated On:

                                               I Spent The Night Before:

Today I Noticed:

                                               Last Night's Dream/Today's Daydream:

Today's Eureka Moment:

Last Night's Sleep Was _____.

HOLD ON, LET'S CONNECT

Date: Season (Name It):   Days In This Season:

I Feel: My Spirit Feels:

Today I Was Pushed To: I Spent Time With God By:

Today I Felt That I Was Being Pulled   Questions I Have:
Away From:

This Season, I Am Seeing: Answers To Questions The Spirit
                                                 Provided:

Today I Meditated On:

                                                 I Spent The Night Before:

Today I Noticed:

                                                 Last Night's Dream/Today's Daydream:

Today's Eureka Moment:

Last Night's Sleep Was _____.

HOLD ON, LET'S CONNECT

Date: Season (Name It):   Days In This Season:

I Feel: My Spirit Feels:

Today I Was Pushed To: I Spent Time With God By:

Today I Felt That I Was Being Pulled   Questions I Have:
Away From:

This Season, I Am Seeing: Answers To Questions The Spirit
                                           Provided:

Today I Meditated On:

                                           I Spent The Night Before:

Today I Noticed:

                                           Last Night's Dream/Today's Daydream:

Today's Eureka Moment:

Last Night's Sleep Was _____.

HOLD ON, LET'S CONNECT

Date: Season (Name It):   Days In This Season:

I Feel: My Spirit Feels:

Today I Was Pushed To: I Spent Time With God By:

Today I Felt That I Was Being Pulled   Questions I Have:
Away From:

This Season, I Am Seeing: Answers To Questions The Spirit
                                                      Provided:

Today I Meditated On:

                                                      I Spent The Night Before:

Today I Noticed:

                                                      Last Night's Dream/Today's Daydream:

Today's Eureka Moment:

Last Night's Sleep Was _____.

HOLD ON, LET'S CONNECT

Date: Season (Name It):   Days In This Season:

I Feel: My Spirit Feels:

Today I Was Pushed To: I Spent Time With God By:

Today I Felt That I Was Being Pulled   Questions I Have:
Away From:

This Season, I Am Seeing: Answers To Questions The Spirit
                                           Provided:

Today I Meditated On:

                                           I Spent The Night Before:

Today I Noticed:

                                           Last Night's Dream/Today's Daydream:

Today's Eureka Moment:

Last Night's Sleep Was _____.

CONNECTED NOTES

(Jot Down Your Thoughts Here)

RIGHT NOW I AM CHOOSING TO REMEMBER AND EMBRACE ...

HOLD ON, LET'S CONNECT

Date: Season (Name It):   Days In This Season:

I Feel: My Spirit Feels:

Today I Was Pushed To: I Spent Time With God By:

Today I Felt That I Was Being Pulled   Questions I Have:
Away From:

This Season, I Am Seeing: Answers To Questions The Spirit
                                           Provided:

Today I Meditated On:

                                           I Spent The Night Before:

Today I Noticed:

                                           Last Night's Dream/Today's Daydream:

Today's Eureka Moment:

Last Night's Sleep Was _____.

HOLD ON, LET'S CONNECT

Date: Season (Name It):   Days In This Season:

I Feel: My Spirit Feels:

Today I Was Pushed To: I Spent Time With God By:

Today I Felt That I Was Being Pulled   Questions I Have:
Away From:

This Season, I Am Seeing: Answers To Questions The Spirit
                                           Provided:

Today I Meditated On:

                                           I Spent The Night Before:

Today I Noticed:

                                           Last Night's Dream/Today's Daydream:

Today's Eureka Moment:

Last Night's Sleep Was _____.

HOLD ON, LET'S CONNECT

Date: Season (Name It):   Days In This Season:

I Feel: My Spirit Feels:

Today I Was Pushed To: I Spent Time With God By:

Today I Felt That I Was Being Pulled   Questions I Have:
Away From:

This Season, I Am Seeing: Answers To Questions The Spirit
                                                      Provided:

Today I Meditated On:

                                                      I Spent The Night Before:

Today I Noticed:

                                                      Last Night's Dream/Today's Daydream:

Today's Eureka Moment:

Last Night's Sleep Was _____.

HOLD ON, LET'S CONNECT

Date: Season (Name It):   Days In This Season:

I Feel:

My Spirit Feels:

Today I Was Pushed To:

I Spent Time With God By:

Today I Felt That I Was Being Pulled
Away From:

Questions I Have:

This Season, I Am Seeing:

Answers To Questions The Spirit
Provided:

Today I Meditated On:

I Spent The Night Before:

Today I Noticed:

Last Night's Dream/Today's Daydream:

Today's Eureka Moment:

Last Night's Sleep Was _____.

I AM FINDING MY TRUTH IN ...

HOLD ON, LET'S CONNECT

Date: Season (Name It):   Days In This Season:

I Feel: My Spirit Feels:

Today I Was Pushed To: I Spent Time With God By:

Today I Felt That I Was Being Pulled   Questions I Have:
Away From:

This Season, I Am Seeing: Answers To Questions The Spirit
                                           Provided:

Today I Meditated On:

                                           I Spent The Night Before:

Today I Noticed:

                                           Last Night's Dream/Today's Daydream:

Today's Eureka Moment:

Last Night's Sleep Was _____.

HOLD ON, LET'S CONNECT

Date: Season (Name It):   Days In This Season:

I Feel:

My Spirit Feels:

Today I Was Pushed To:

I Spent Time With God By:

Today I Felt That I Was Being Pulled
Away From:

Questions I Have:

This Season, I Am Seeing:

Answers To Questions The Spirit
Provided:

Today I Meditated On:

I Spent The Night Before:

Today I Noticed:

Last Night's Dream/Today's Daydream:

Today's Eureka Moment:

Last Night's Sleep Was _____.

HOLD ON, LET'S CONNECT

Date: Season (Name It):   Days In This Season:

I Feel: My Spirit Feels:

Today I Was Pushed To: I Spent Time With God By:

Today I Felt That I Was Being Pulled   Questions I Have:
Away From:

This Season, I Am Seeing: Answers To Questions The Spirit
                                                 Provided:

Today I Meditated On:

                                                 I Spent The Night Before:

Today I Noticed:

                                                 Last Night's Dream/Today's Daydream:

Today's Eureka Moment:

Last Night's Sleep Was _____.

HOLD ON, LET'S CONNECT

Date: Season (Name It):   Days In This Season:

I Feel:	My Spirit Feels:
Today I Was Pushed To:	I Spent Time With God By:
Today I Felt That I Was Being Pulled Away From:	Questions I Have:
This Season, I Am Seeing:	Answers To Questions The Spirit Provided:
Today I Meditated On:	
	I Spent The Night Before:
Today I Noticed:	
	Last Night's Dream/Today's Daydream:
Today's Eureka Moment:	

Last Night's Sleep Was _____.

HOLD ON, LET'S CONNECT

Date: Season (Name It):   Days In This Season:

I Feel: My Spirit Feels:

Today I Was Pushed To: I Spent Time With God By:

Today I Felt That I Was Being Pulled   Questions I Have:
Away From:

This Season, I Am Seeing: Answers To Questions The Spirit
                                                Provided:

Today I Meditated On:

                                                I Spent The Night Before:

Today I Noticed:

                                                Last Night's Dream/Today's Daydream:

Today's Eureka Moment:

Last Night's Sleep Was _____.

CONNECTED NOTES

(Jot Down Your Thoughts Here)

HOLD ON, LET'S CONNECT

Date: Season (Name It):   Days In This Season:

I Feel: | My Spirit Feels:

Today I Was Pushed To: | I Spent Time With God By:

Today I Felt That I Was Being Pulled | Questions I Have:
Away From:

This Season, I Am Seeing: | Answers To Questions The Spirit
                                           | Provided:

Today I Meditated On:

                                           | I Spent The Night Before:

Today I Noticed:

                                           | Last Night's Dream/Today's Daydream:

Today's Eureka Moment:

Last Night's Sleep Was _____.

HOLD ON, LET'S CONNECT

Date: Season (Name It):   Days In This Season:

I Feel: My Spirit Feels:

Today I Was Pushed To: I Spent Time With God By:

Today I Felt That I Was Being Pulled   Questions I Have:
Away From:

This Season, I Am Seeing: Answers To Questions The Spirit
                                                 Provided:

Today I Meditated On:

                                                 I Spent The Night Before:

Today I Noticed:

                                                 Last Night's Dream/Today's Daydream:

Today's Eureka Moment:

Last Night's Sleep Was _____.

HOLD ON, LET'S CONNECT

Date: Season (Name It):   Days In This Season:

I Feel: My Spirit Feels:

Today I Was Pushed To: I Spent Time With God By:

Today I Felt That I Was Being Pulled   Questions I Have:
Away From:

This Season, I Am Seeing: Answers To Questions The Spirit
                                                       Provided:

Today I Meditated On:

                                                       I Spent The Night Before:

Today I Noticed:

                                                       Last Night's Dream/Today's Daydream:

Today's Eureka Moment:

Last Night's Sleep Was _____.

HOLD ON, LET'S CONNECT

Date: Season (Name It):   Days In This Season:

I Feel: My Spirit Feels:

Today I Was Pushed To: I Spent Time With God By:

Today I Felt That I Was Being Pulled   Questions I Have:
Away From:

This Season, I Am Seeing: Answers To Questions The Spirit
                                                   Provided:

Today I Meditated On:

                                                   I Spent The Night Before:

Today I Noticed:

                                                   Last Night's Dream/Today's Daydream:

Today's Eureka Moment:

Last Night's Sleep Was _____.

I CALL THIS PERIOD OF MY LIFE ...

HOLD ON, LET'S CONNECT

Date: Season (Name It):   Days In This Season:

I Feel: | My Spirit Feels:

Today I Was Pushed To: | I Spent Time With God By:

Today I Felt That I Was Being Pulled | Questions I Have:
Away From:

This Season, I Am Seeing: | Answers To Questions The Spirit
                                           | Provided:

Today I Meditated On:

                                           | I Spent The Night Before:

Today I Noticed:

                                           | Last Night's Dream/Today's Daydream:

Today's Eureka Moment:

Last Night's Sleep Was _____.

HOLD ON, LET'S CONNECT

Date: Season (Name It):   Days In This Season:

I Feel: My Spirit Feels:

Today I Was Pushed To: I Spent Time With God By:

Today I Felt That I Was Being Pulled   Questions I Have:
Away From:

This Season, I Am Seeing: Answers To Questions The Spirit
                                                      Provided:

Today I Meditated On:

                                                      I Spent The Night Before:

Today I Noticed:

                                                      Last Night's Dream/Today's Daydream:

Today's Eureka Moment:

Last Night's Sleep Was _____.

HOLD ON, LET'S CONNECT

Date: Season (Name It):   Days In This Season:

I Feel: My Spirit Feels:

Today I Was Pushed To: I Spent Time With God By:

Today I Felt That I Was Being Pulled   Questions I Have:
Away From:

This Season, I Am Seeing: Answers To Questions The Spirit
                                                  Provided:

Today I Meditated On:

                                                  I Spent The Night Before:

Today I Noticed:

                                                  Last Night's Dream/Today's Daydream:

Today's Eureka Moment:

Last Night's Sleep Was _____.

HOLD ON, LET'S CONNECT

Date: Season (Name It):   Days In This Season:

I Feel: My Spirit Feels:

Today I Was Pushed To: I Spent Time With God By:

Today I Felt That I Was Being Pulled   Questions I Have:
Away From:

This Season, I Am Seeing: Answers To Questions The Spirit
                                           Provided:

Today I Meditated On:

                                           I Spent The Night Before:

Today I Noticed:

                                           Last Night's Dream/Today's Daydream:

Today's Eureka Moment:

Last Night's Sleep Was _____.

I AM SHIFTING INTO A HIGHER LEVEL OF SELF.

HOLD ON, LET'S CONNECT

Date:　　　　　Season (Name It):　　　　　Days In This Season:

I Feel:

My Spirit Feels:

Today I Was Pushed To:

I Spent Time With God By:

Today I Felt That I Was Being Pulled Away From:

Questions I Have:

This Season, I Am Seeing:

Answers To Questions The Spirit Provided:

Today I Meditated On:

I Spent The Night Before:

Today I Noticed:

Last Night's Dream/Today's Daydream:

Today's Eureka Moment:

Last Night's Sleep Was _____.

HOLD ON, LET'S CONNECT

Date: Season (Name It):   Days In This Season:

I Feel: My Spirit Feels:

Today I Was Pushed To: I Spent Time With God By:

Today I Felt That I Was Being Pulled   Questions I Have:
Away From:

This Season, I Am Seeing: Answers To Questions The Spirit
                                                 Provided:

Today I Meditated On:

                                                 I Spent The Night Before:

Today I Noticed:

                                                 Last Night's Dream/Today's Daydream:

Today's Eureka Moment:

Last Night's Sleep Was _____.

HOLD ON, LET'S CONNECT

Date: Season (Name It):   Days In This Season:

I Feel: My Spirit Feels:

Today I Was Pushed To: I Spent Time With God By:

Today I Felt That I Was Being Pulled   Questions I Have:
Away From:

This Season, I Am Seeing: Answers To Questions The Spirit
                                                 Provided:

Today I Meditated On:

                                                 I Spent The Night Before:

Today I Noticed:

                                                 Last Night's Dream/Today's Daydream:

Today's Eureka Moment:

Last Night's Sleep Was _____.

I AM REALIZING IT'S TIME TO LET GO.

HOLD ON, LET'S CONNECT

Date: Season (Name It):   Days In This Season:

I Feel: My Spirit Feels:

Today I Was Pushed To: I Spent Time With God By:

Today I Felt That I Was Being Pulled   Questions I Have:
Away From:

This Season, I Am Seeing: Answers To Questions The Spirit
                                       Provided:

Today I Meditated On:

                                       I Spent The Night Before:

Today I Noticed:

                                       Last Night's Dream/Today's Daydream:

Today's Eureka Moment:

Last Night's Sleep Was _____.

HOLD ON, LET'S CONNECT

Date: Season (Name It):   Days In This Season:

I Feel: My Spirit Feels:

Today I Was Pushed To: I Spent Time With God By:

Today I Felt That I Was Being Pulled   Questions I Have:
Away From:

This Season, I Am Seeing: Answers To Questions The Spirit
                                            Provided:

Today I Meditated On:

                                            I Spent The Night Before:

Today I Noticed:

                                            Last Night's Dream/Today's Daydream:

Today's Eureka Moment:

Last Night's Sleep Was _____.

HOLD ON, LET'S CONNECT

Date: Season (Name It):   Days In This Season:

I Feel: My Spirit Feels:

Today I Was Pushed To: I Spent Time With God By:

Today I Felt That I Was Being Pulled   Questions I Have:
Away From:

This Season, I Am Seeing: Answers To Questions The Spirit
                                                    Provided:

Today I Meditated On:

                                                    I Spent The Night Before:

Today I Noticed:

                                                    Last Night's Dream/Today's Daydream:

Today's Eureka Moment:

Last Night's Sleep Was _____.

HOLD ON, LET'S CONNECT

Date: Season (Name It):   Days In This Season:

I Feel: My Spirit Feels:

Today I Was Pushed To: I Spent Time With God By:

Today I Felt That I Was Being Pulled   Questions I Have:
Away From:

This Season, I Am Seeing: Answers To Questions The Spirit
                                           Provided:

Today I Meditated On:

                                           I Spent The Night Before:

Today I Noticed:

                                           Last Night's Dream/Today's Daydream:

Today's Eureka Moment:

Last Night's Sleep Was _____.

MY
SPIRIT
SAYS NO.
MY
SPIRIT
SAYS YES.

Made in the USA
Columbia, SC
20 February 2019